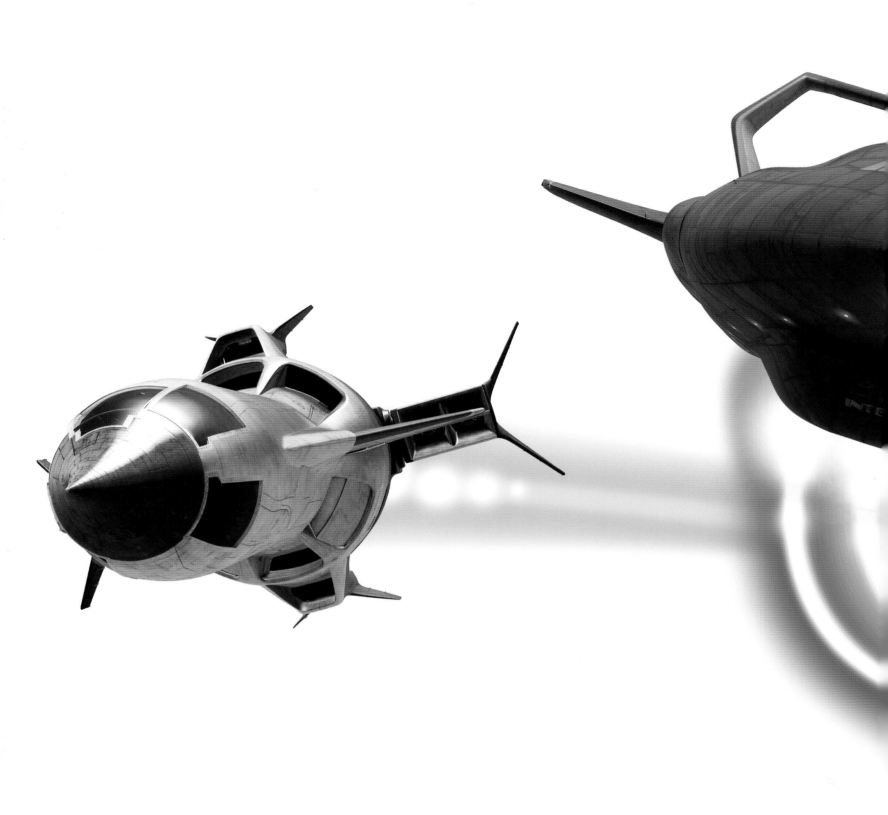

THUNDERBIRDS ™

X-RAY CROSS-SECTIONS

Alex Pang

OXFORD

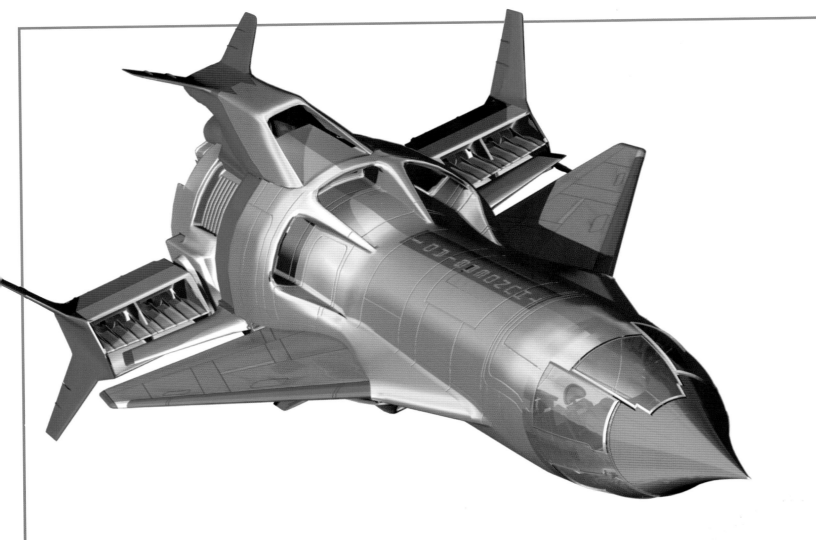

OXFORD
UNIVERSITY PRESS

Great Clarendon Street, Oxford OX2 6DP

Oxford University Press is a department of the University of Oxford.
It furthers the University's objective of excellence in research, scholarship,
and education by publishing worldwide in

Oxford New York

Auckland Bangkok Buenos Aires Cape Town Chennai
Dar es Salaam Delhi Hong Kong Istanbul Karachi Kolkata
Kuala Lumpur Madrid Melbourne Mexico City Mumbai Nairobi
São Paulo Shanghai Taipei Tokyo Toronto

Oxford is a registered trade mark of Oxford University Press
in the UK and in certain other countries

Illustrations by Alex Pang
Text by Jon Richards
Design by Jane Hannath

First published 2004

UNIVERSAL STUDIOS
CONSUMER PRODUCTS GROUP

www.universalstudios.com

British Library Cataloguing in Publication Data available

ISBN 0 19 911249 5

1 3 5 7 9 10 8 6 4 2

Printed in Italy

CONTENTS

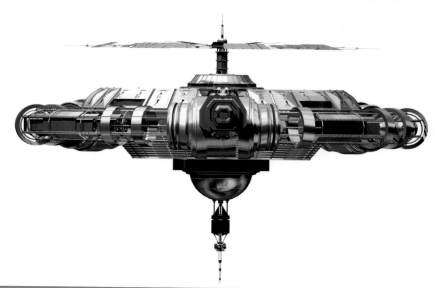

TRACY ISLAND

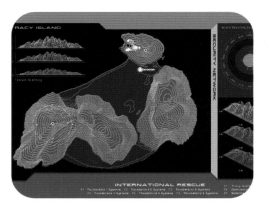

Situated in the sparkling blue waters of the Pacific Ocean is the headquarters of International Rescue. Tracy Island is the peak of an extinct sea volcano, and its secluded location far out in the Pacific helps to maintain the all-important secrecy of the rescue organization. The surface of the island has the 'normal' appearance of a millionaire's holiday home, but its volcanic past means that there are plenty of subterranean chambers that are perfect for hangars, production factories and laboratories.

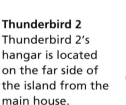

Thunderbird 2
Thunderbird 2's hangar is located on the far side of the island from the main house.

04

Paradise on Earth

The main surface buildings are located on the lowest of the island's three peaks, and they maintain the island's façade as a millionaire's paradise home. Other buildings scattered on this peak include the Round House, which sits on the summit. The central part of the island is a nature reserve whose lush tropical forest is home to a wide variety of plants and animals, some of which are unique to Tracy Island. On top of the third and tallest peak of the island is International Rescue's communications array. This uses secure frequencies to send and receive signals to and from the Thunderbirds fleet.

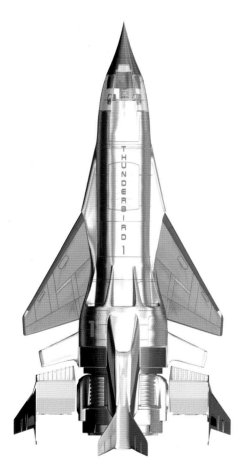

Pool-side
Tracy Island is fitted out with every kind of luxury and leisure feature, ensuring that the International Rescue team can relax after a strenuous mission.

Thunderbird 1
Thunderbird 1 blasts clear of Tracy Island from its hangar hidden beneath the swimming pool in front of the main house.

Thunderbird 3
The island's peace and quiet are shattered when Thunderbird 3 blasts clear from its launch pad beneath the Round House.

Thunderbird 5
Thousands of kilometres above the luxury of Tracy Island, International Rescue's monitoring station, Thunderbird 5, travels in its fixed orbit.

Tracy Island
...parating the three peaks of Tracy ...and are large areas of silvery sand, ...aking it the perfect picture-book ...radise island.

Thunderbird 4
Thunderbird 4 is on permanent standby inside Thunderbird 2 on the far side of the island.

GOOD GUYS, BAD GUYS

THUNDERBIRDS HEROES AND VILLAINS

Following the death of his wife in a tragic accident, billionaire astronaut Jeff Tracy resigned from NASA and left with his five young sons (Scott, Virgil, Gordon, John and Alan) for a remote and deserted tropical island. He was determined to use all his abilities and his huge wealth to stop such an experience happening to anybody else. So with the help of scientific genius 'Brains' Hackenbacker, he created the Thunderbirds, a fleet of high-tech machines designed to cope with all emergencies in any part of the globe.

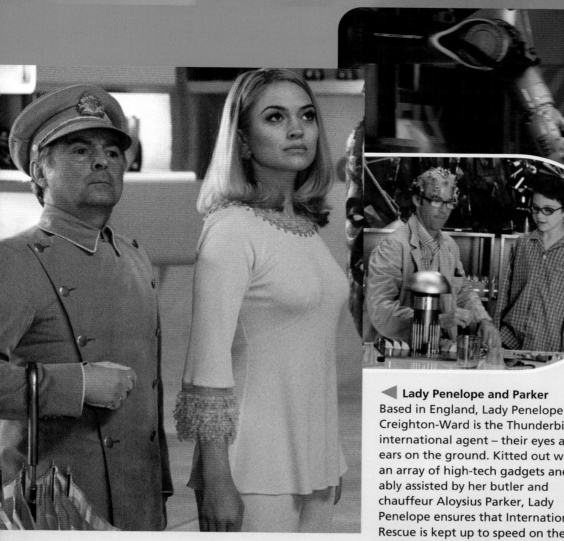

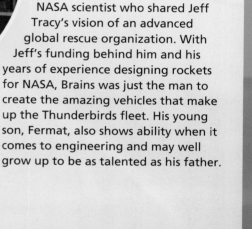

Brains and Fermat
'Brains' Hackenbacker is a former NASA scientist who shared Jeff Tracy's vision of an advanced global rescue organization. With Jeff's funding behind him and his years of experience designing rockets for NASA, Brains was just the man to create the amazing vehicles that make up the Thunderbirds fleet. His young son, Fermat, also shows ability when it comes to engineering and may well grow up to be as talented as his father.

Lady Penelope and Parker
Based in England, Lady Penelope Creighton-Ward is the Thunderbirds international agent – their eyes and ears on the ground. Kitted out with an array of high-tech gadgets and ably assisted by her butler and chauffeur Aloysius Parker, Lady Penelope ensures that International Rescue is kept up to speed on the latest world developments.

Our heroes
Gordon, John, Jeff, Scott and Virgil

The Hood
The Hood is a man with a grudge. When his illegal diamond mine in the jungles of Malaya collapsed, International Rescue rushed to the scene, pulling out all of the survivors – except one: the Hood was left behind, presumed dead. Now he's back, determined to get revenge on the organization that deserted him in the jungle.

Transom
With a smile that would make any dentist nervous, Transom is the Hood's scientific brains. Although no match for Mr Hackenbacker in the intelligence department, she has proved invaluable to the evil Hood, developing his stealth submarine and a whole host of other devilish devices.

More heroes
Tintin, Alan and Fermat

Mullion
A former pro-wrestler, Mullion was hired by the Hood to provide the muscle behind his evil plans. He is far from being a mindless hulk, however, with degrees in engineering and biomechanics and an astonishing ability to handle almost any vehicle put in front of him.

THUNDERBIRD 1

INTERNATIONAL RESCUE'S RAPID-RESPONSE VEHICLE

Speed is vital in an emergency, and they don't come any faster than International Rescue's rapid-response vehicle. Thunderbird 1 has been designed to reach the site of an emergency in the shortest possible time, collect information, and assess the situation while the other Thunderbirds are on the way. It is fitted with cutting-edge technology in the form of advanced aerodynamics and jet engines that are able to blast it through the air at unbelievable speeds and to the very edge of space.

Stealth shape and coating

Thunderbird 1's unique body shape gives it 'stealth capabilities' – it has been specially designed to scatter radar signals rather than reflect them back to a receiver. Its body is also coated in a top-secret material – a polymer resin – designed and created by Brains in the International Rescue laboratories. This resin absorbs up to 75% of a radar wave's energy. Combined with the anti-detection device in the nose cone, these features make Thunderbird 1 totally invisible to any conventional detection device.

Starboard wing

Hinge mounting for swing wings

Intake vents for forward Hackenbacker VTOL engine. These remain closed during normal flight and are opened for vertical take-off and landing (VTOL) and for hovering.

Plexiglass cockpit canopy. Designed to withstand collision with objects at supersonic speeds.

Hackenbacker VTOL engine. Thunderbird 1 is fitted with two of these, and they are used for slow flight or during vertical take-off and landing.

Pilot seat

Cockpit with capacity for a crew of two

Anti-detection device. Gives out an FM (frequency-modulating) radio wave that can alter its pitch to match and blank out an incoming radar signal.

Nose cone

Titanium alloy framework

Nose undercarriage

Co-pilot seat. Thunderbird 1 can be flown by one crew member, so a co-pilot is not essential.

Multi-purpose cannon. Usually stored inside Thunderbird 1's fuselage, this powerful cannon drops down through the lower hatch when in use.

Anti blow-out tyres

Exhaust for VTOL engine. This can be directed using a 'thrust-vectoring' system so that the pilot can steer Thunderbird 1 at slow speeds for delicate rescue manoeuvres.

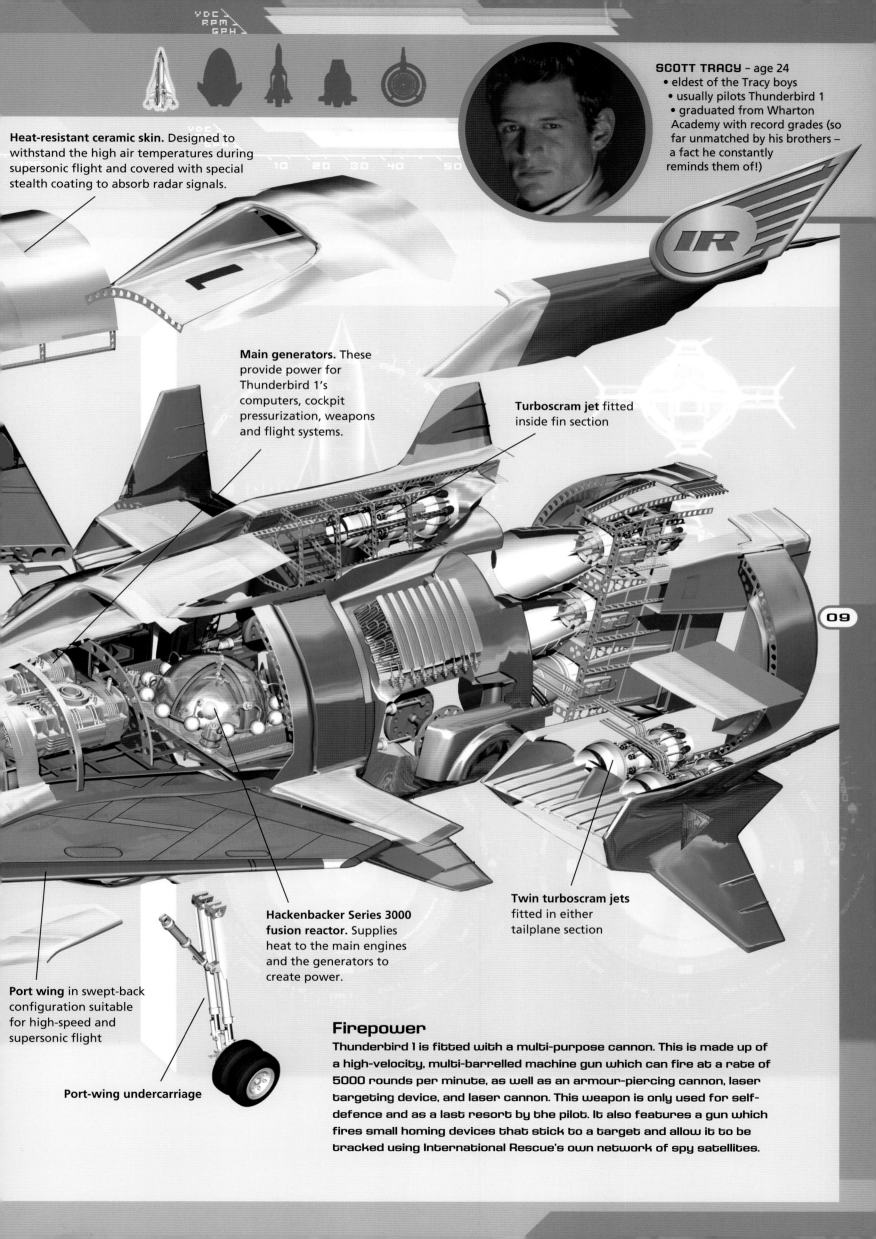

Heat-resistant ceramic skin. Designed to withstand the high air temperatures during supersonic flight and covered with special stealth coating to absorb radar signals.

SCOTT TRACY – age 24
• eldest of the Tracy boys
• usually pilots Thunderbird 1
• graduated from Wharton Academy with record grades (so far unmatched by his brothers – a fact he constantly reminds them of!)

Main generators. These provide power for Thunderbird 1's computers, cockpit pressurization, weapons and flight systems.

Turboscram jet fitted inside fin section

Hackenbacker Series 3000 fusion reactor. Supplies heat to the main engines and the generators to create power.

Twin turboscram jets fitted in either tailplane section

Port wing in swept-back configuration suitable for high-speed and supersonic flight

Port-wing undercarriage

Firepower

Thunderbird 1 is fitted with a multi-purpose cannon. This is made up of a high-velocity, multi-barrelled machine gun which can fire at a rate of 5000 rounds per minute, as well as an armour-piercing cannon, laser targeting device, and laser cannon. This weapon is only used for self-defence and as a last resort by the pilot. It also features a gun which fires small homing devices that stick to a target and allow it to be tracked using International Rescue's own network of spy satellites.

Swinging wings

Thunderbird 1 uses a system known as variable geometry, or 'swing wings'. At low speeds, the pilot swings the wings out wide. In this position, the wings provide the maximum amount of lift. At high speeds, the pilot pulls the wings into the body. This gives the aircraft a dart shape that is ideal for supersonic flight.

Wings extended to maximum angle

Wings drawn back into fuselage

10

Intakes for turboscram jets

Turboscram jets

Thunderbird 1 is powered by one of Brains Hackenbacker's many inventions – the turboscram jet. At low speeds, this engine acts like a normal jet, using turbines to suck in and compress vast amounts of air. Fuel is then added and the mixture set alight to create a jet of hot gas that pushes the aircraft forward. As Thunderbird 1 goes past the sound barrier, it does not need to use its turbines – at these speeds the air is at enormous pressure anyway. By adding fuel and setting light to this supersonic airflow, the turboscram jet engines blast Thunderbird 1 forward at several times the speed of sound.

Tree hugger

Thunderbird 1 is fitted with a downward-pointing radar array which is used to read the contours of the ground below. This information is then sent to the main computer, which can make minor course adjustments and prevent the aircraft from crashing during low-level flight.

HOVER POWER

Thunderbirds 1 and 2 are fitted with Hackenbacker VTOL engines, which allow the aircraft to take off and land vertically and to hover. These powerful jet engines draw in air from above the aircraft and, like a normal jet engine, compress it, add fuel and set the mixture alight to produce a jet of hot gases. The direction of this jet can be controlled by the pilot to guide the aircraft down to earth in a tricky landing zone.

▶ Thanks to Thunderbird 1's advanced automated piloting and navigation systems, even an untrained pilot like Alan Tracy can fly the aircraft. Which is fortunate, as he and Fermat Hackenbacker are the last people who can stop the evil Hood from robbing the world's major banks.

Escape pod
In the event of an explosion, the pilot does not eject as in a normal jet – at the high speeds at which Thunderbird 1 travels, such a move would be suicidal. Instead, the entire cockpit section is blasted clear and drag parachutes are used to slow the escape pod and guide it safely back down to earth.

wingspan 18.3 metres

length 33 metres

High flier
Thunderbird 1 is able to fly at such a high altitude that it is effectively in orbit. The aircraft's engines and aerodynamics have been specially designed to cope with conditions at these extreme altitudes, where the air is very thin and conventional aircraft would find it impossible to fly.

Heavy-duty glider
Despite its size and weight, Thunderbird 1 has been designed to glide. Should the engines fail or if a stealthy approach is required, the pilot can fly the aircraft in a similar way to a conventional glider.

TECHNICAL DATA

Crew	up to 2
Length	33 metres (108 feet)
Width of fuselage	3.8 metres (12.5 feet)
Wingspan with wings extended	18.3 metres (60 feet)
Weight	135 tonnes
Maximum speed	24,150 km/h (15,000 mph)
Power source	Hackenbacker series 3000 fusion reactor
Range	unlimited
Engines	5 thrust-vectored turboscram jets (2 fitted in each horizontal section of the tailplane; 1 in the fin) 2 Hackenbacker VTOL engines
Armaments	multi-barrelled cannon

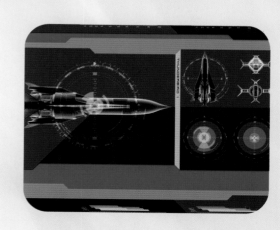

THUNDERBIRD 2

The first vehicle of the Thunderbirds fleet to be planned by Jeff Tracy and his scientific consultant Brains, Thunderbird 2 is the heavy-lifting tool for International Rescue. Thunderbird 2 was designed around its two enormous cargo pod areas and built to carry vital equipment to and from an emergency as quickly as possible. The size and complexity of the craft meant that it took longer to build than Thunderbird 1, and the green giant was second off the line at International Rescue's automated production plant – hence its name.

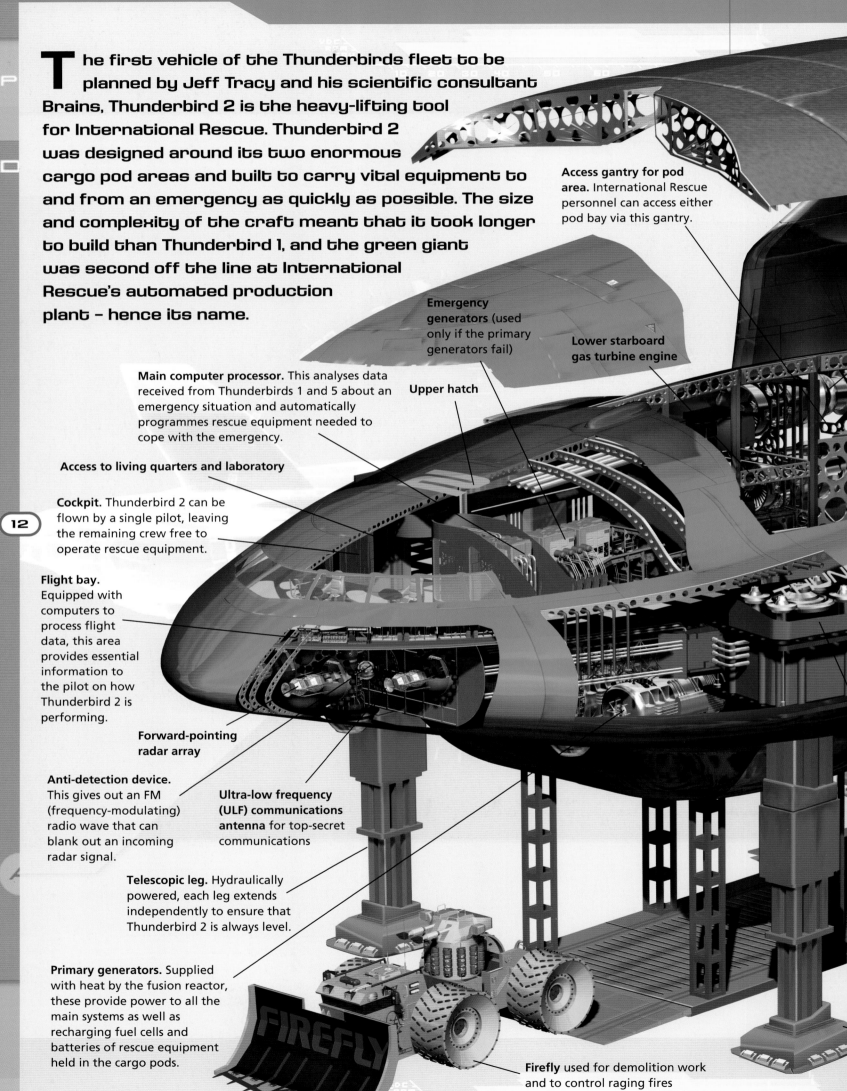

Access gantry for pod area. International Rescue personnel can access either pod bay via this gantry.

Emergency generators (used only if the primary generators fail)

Lower starboard gas turbine engine

Main computer processor. This analyses data received from Thunderbirds 1 and 5 about an emergency situation and automatically programmes rescue equipment needed to cope with the emergency.

Upper hatch

Access to living quarters and laboratory

Cockpit. Thunderbird 2 can be flown by a single pilot, leaving the remaining crew free to operate rescue equipment.

Flight bay. Equipped with computers to process flight data, this area provides essential information to the pilot on how Thunderbird 2 is performing.

Forward-pointing radar array

Anti-detection device. This gives out an FM (frequency-modulating) radio wave that can blank out an incoming radar signal.

Ultra-low frequency (ULF) communications antenna for top-secret communications

Telescopic leg. Hydraulically powered, each leg extends independently to ensure that Thunderbird 2 is always level.

Primary generators. Supplied with heat by the fusion reactor, these provide power to all the main systems as well as recharging fuel cells and batteries of rescue equipment held in the cargo pods.

Firefly used for demolition work and to control raging fires

12

VIRGIL TRACY – age 20
• usually pilots Thunderbird 2
• the fitness fanatic of the family, generally to be found in the Tracy Island gym • when off duty, takes part in triathlons and other sporting events

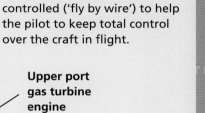

Pod area maintenance and programming station. Instructions from the main computer processor are routed through this terminal to programme rescue equipment.

Upper starboard gas turbine engine

Fuel tanks

Hackenbacker series 3000 fusion reactor providing heat to the engines and generators.

Tail section. The air control surfaces at the rear of Thunderbird 2 are computer-controlled ('fly by wire') to help the pilot to keep total control over the craft in flight.

Upper port gas turbine engine

Hackenbacker VTOL engine. Thunderbird 2 is fitted with four of these. Their thrust can be directed by a 'thrust-vectoring' system so that the pilot can steer the aircraft at slow speeds.

Port swept-forward wing. The forward sweep of the wings gives Thunderbird 2 extra stability in flight.

Air intake for Hackenbacker VTOL engine (usually sealed during normal flight)

Air intakes

Fuel and power lines

Titanium alloy framework

Telescopic ramp leg. These legs extend to lower rescue equipment from the pod bays.

Fluid reservoir for telescopic leg hydraulics

Primary pod ramp

Secondary pod area. Thunderbird 4 is always stored in this area.

All-terrain landing foot. Heavy-duty caterpillar tracks fitted to the feet allow the pilot to move Thunderbird 2 while the legs are extended.

Going up

Thunderbird 2 owes its squat frame to technology developed by NASA in the 1960s – technology that went into the design of the Space Shuttle. 'Borrowed' from NASA, this technology has been further developed by Brains in the International Rescue laboratories, reaching a pinnacle in Thunderbird 2's design.

Normal wide-bodied aircraft use their wings alone to provide lift and so need long wings to get them off the ground. This makes them much wider from wingtip to wingtip and more difficult to control. Thunderbird 2, on the other hand, gets most of its lift from the shape of its body and only requires short wings. As a result, Thunderbird 2 has a far wider body frame in comparison to normal aircraft, enabling it to carry larger and heavier loads.

13

THUNDERBIRD 2

LIFTING OFF WITH THE GREEN GIANT

Thunderbird 4 is stored in the secondary pod area and can be launched from a hydraulic ramp that pitches the craft forward as Thunderbird 2 hovers just above the water. Thunderbird 2 can then move on quickly with other equipment it is carrying to another danger zone. In the event of a high-altitude launch, Thunderbird 4 is fitted with a parafoil – a type of steerable parachute, which allows the pilot to guide the submarine safely down to the surface of the water.

FEEL THE BURN

Except for Thunderbird 4, all of International Rescue's major vehicles are powered by a Hackenbacker series 3000 fusion reactor. Deep inside the reactor's many layers of protective shielding, atoms are crushed together, unleashing massive amounts of energy (it's the same process that powers the Sun!). This energy is released as heat and channelled to the engines and generators.

▶ Despite its titanic proportions, Thunderbird 2 can still be controlled with pinpoint accuracy. Its VTOL engines give precise control, allowing the pilot to perform even the most delicate manoeuvres – essential for picking up personnel from a blazing oil rig and depositing them at the nearest hospital for emergency treatment.

Brains's big baby
Thunderbird 2 is the culmination of years of work by Brains Hackenbacker. He has succeeded in combining a truly unique design with some of the world's strongest materials. The result is this mighty aircraft – the tireless workhorse of the International Rescue fleet.

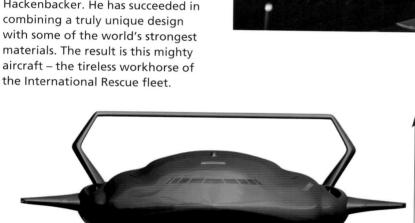

height 17 metres

Gentle giant
This massive rescue aircraft is nearly as long as 10 buses placed end to end. When raised on its telescopic legs, it is as tall as a 10-storey building and, fully laden, it weighs over 100 tonnes more than a jumbo jet.

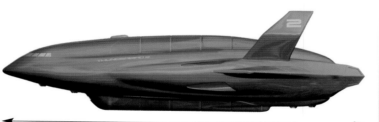

length 71 metres

wingspan 51 metres

Strong but clean
Thunderbird 2 may be the most powerful aircraft of its type in the world, but it is also one of the cleanest. Thanks to its environmentally friendly gas turbine engines and its fusion reactor, the green giant produces less pollution than a medium-sized family car.

TECHNICAL DATA

Crew	up to 5 (pilot and co-pilot, plus crew to operate emergency equipment)
Length	71 metres (233 feet)
Wingspan	51 metres (167 feet)
Width of fuselage	38 metres (125 feet)
Height	17 metres (56 feet)
with legs extended	31 metres (102 feet)
Weight	
without payload	426 tonnes
Maximum payload	137 tonnes
Maximum speed	9177 km/h (5700 mph)
Power source	Hackenbacker series 3000 fusion reactor
Range	unlimited
Engines	4 gas turbine engines 4 Hackenbacker VTOL engines
Armaments	none

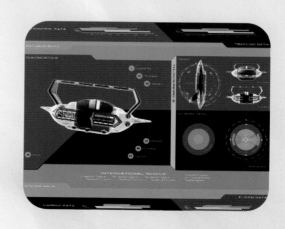

POD VEHICLES

INTERNATIONAL RESCUE'S SPECIALIST EQUIPMENT

Thunderbird 2's massive primary pod area is big enough to carry the largest emergency vehicle – which is just as well, as Brains has designed a whole host of rescue vehicles to suit every type of emergency. These include heavy-lift cranes, designed to move the largest obstacles; powerful tunnelling machines; fire-fighting vehicles; and mobile, heavy-duty laser cutters. Shown here is just a small sample of Mr Hackenbacker's ingenious inventions.

▼ The Thunderizer

The enormous barrel on top of the Thunderizer is actually a cannon, which fires a beam of charged particles at an obstruction. This beam shatters anything in its path but leaves any organic matter – including people – untouched and unharmed. This makes the vehicle perfect for reaching trapped people in a hurry.

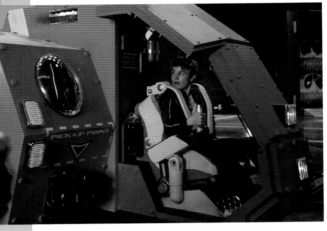

▲ Alan uses the Thunderizer to blast an escape route through to Thunderbird 1's hangar.

16

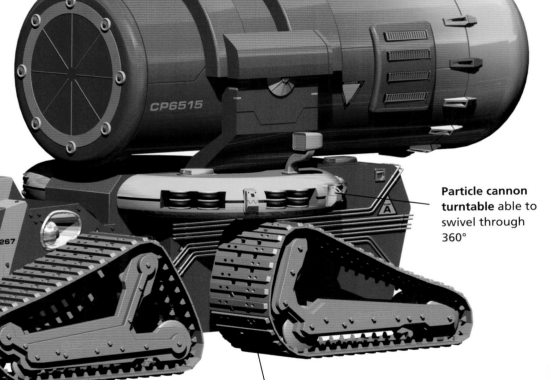

Particle cannon used to fire a beam of charged particles at an obstruction

Particle cannon turntable able to swivel through 360°

Caterpillar tracks suitable for the roughest terrain

Thunderizer cockpit slung low against the main chassis to stay out of the way of the charged particle beam

► Tintin prepares to blast the bad guys with a high-pressure jet of flame-retardant foam.

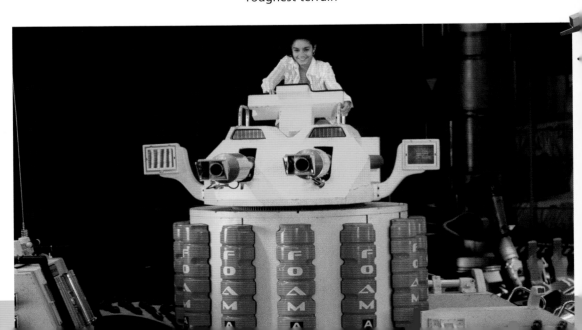

Cutting teeth
on drill bit

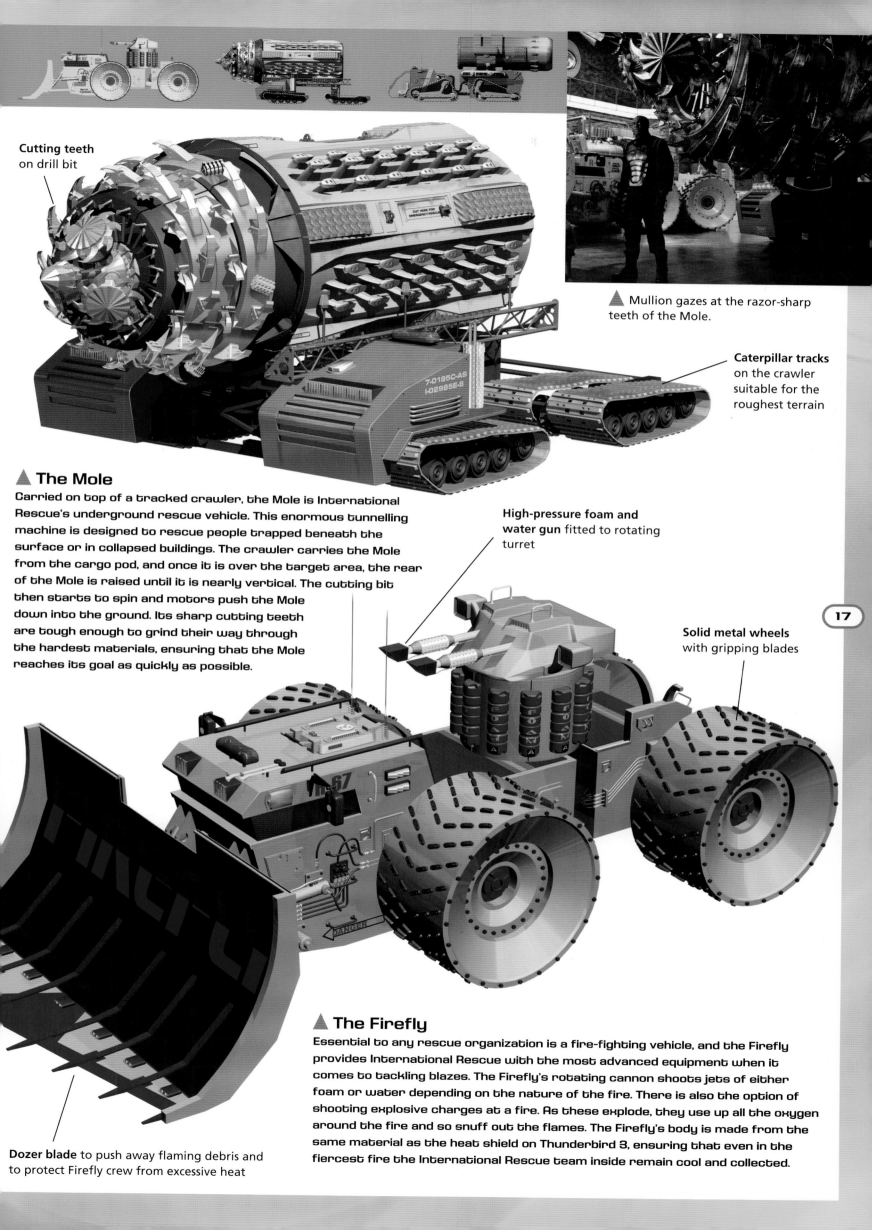

▲ Mullion gazes at the razor-sharp teeth of the Mole.

Caterpillar tracks
on the crawler suitable for the roughest terrain

▲ The Mole

Carried on top of a tracked crawler, the Mole is International Rescue's underground rescue vehicle. This enormous tunnelling machine is designed to rescue people trapped beneath the surface or in collapsed buildings. The crawler carries the Mole from the cargo pod, and once it is over the target area, the rear of the Mole is raised until it is nearly vertical. The cutting bit then starts to spin and motors push the Mole down into the ground. Its sharp cutting teeth are tough enough to grind their way through the hardest materials, ensuring that the Mole reaches its goal as quickly as possible.

High-pressure foam and water gun fitted to rotating turret

Solid metal wheels with gripping blades

▲ The Firefly

Essential to any rescue organization is a fire-fighting vehicle, and the Firefly provides International Rescue with the most advanced equipment when it comes to tackling blazes. The Firefly's rotating cannon shoots jets of either foam or water depending on the nature of the fire. There is also the option of shooting explosive charges at a fire. As these explode, they use up all the oxygen around the fire and so snuff out the flames. The Firefly's body is made from the same material as the heat shield on Thunderbird 3, ensuring that even in the fiercest fire the International Rescue team inside remain cool and collected.

Dozer blade to push away flaming debris and to protect Firefly crew from excessive heat

THUNDERBIRD 3

INTERNATIONAL RESCUE'S DEEP-SPACE ROCKET

Space steering

Because there is no air in space, rockets cannot use control surfaces such as rudders and ailerons as normal aircraft do. Instead, the body of Thunderbird 3 is equipped with a number of small 'attitude-control' rockets that are used only when the spacecraft is beyond the Earth's atmosphere. These tiny rockets are fired to adjust the rocket's path in three directions: side to side (yaw), up and down (pitch), and around its central axis (roll).

Coolant tanks for rocket engine casing. Coolant is pumped around the engine's casing and exhaust nozzle to prevent them from overheating and cracking with the extreme temperatures.

Oxidizer tanks for rocket engines

Hackenbacker series 3000 fusion reactor providing heat for the main generators

Exhaust for rocket engines

Combustion chamber for rocket engine. Inside these chambers the propellant and oxidizer are mixed and ignited to create the rocket's thrust.

Buttress fin to increase stability during atmospheric flight

Gimbal mount for rocket engine. This allows the rocket engine to be moved slightly in order to steer Thunderbird 3.

Main body rocket engines

Buttress rocket engine

Propellant tanks for main rocket engines

Supporting buttress

Coolant tanks for reactor casing. A continuous flow of coolant is required to prevent the core from overheating, which could lead to meltdown.

Main generator providing power for computer, navigation and life-support systems

18

Thrust control

Trying to steer a powerful rocket such as Thunderbird 3 while it is blasting high into the atmosphere is no easy task. To maintain control over their direction of flight, rockets use a variety of systems, including smaller 'thrust motors', which direct the thrust of the main engines, and 'gimbal mountings'. Gimbals are movable mountings on which the rocket engines themselves are swung in different directions to steer the rocket.

GORDON TRACY – age 18
• recently graduated from
Wharton Academy
• still training on the
Thunderbirds craft, will be
another year before he
can fly solo

As a trained astronaut himself, Jeff Tracy always knew about the dangers of space travel and the need for International Rescue to offer a rescue service beyond the limits of the Earth's atmosphere. And once he had decided on an orbiting space platform (later Thunderbird 5) from which IR could monitor events on the ground, it was clear that a craft was needed that could travel into space. Thunderbird 3 fulfils these roles as a shuttle vehicle to Thunderbird 5 and as a deep-space rescue vehicle. It is powerful enough to comfortably reach Earth orbit and to blast further into space, if the need should arise.

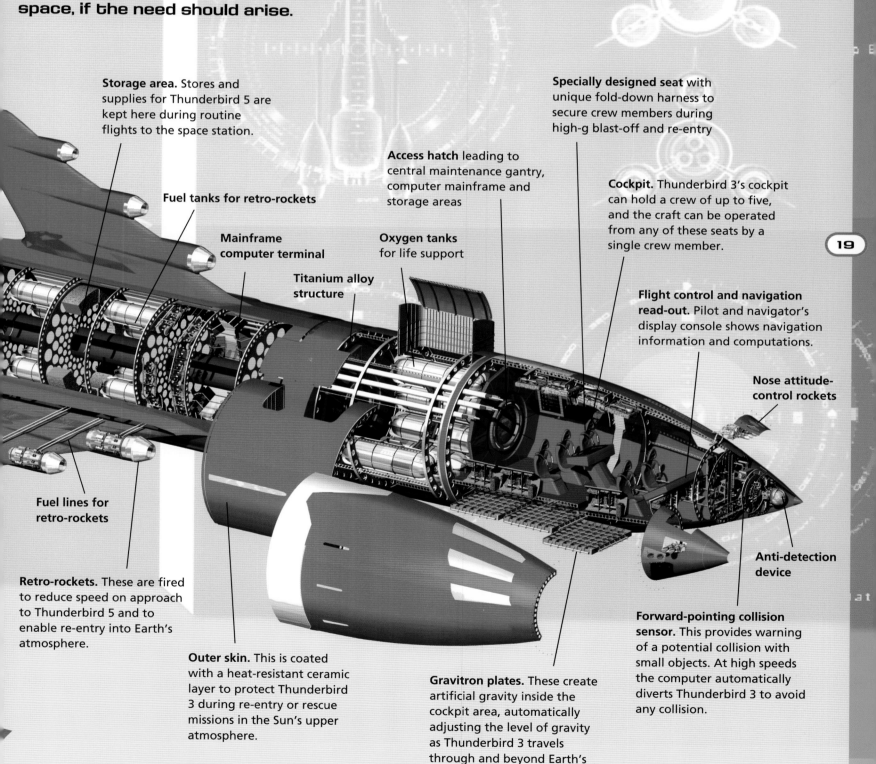

Storage area. Stores and supplies for Thunderbird 5 are kept here during routine flights to the space station.

Fuel tanks for retro-rockets

Mainframe computer terminal

Titanium alloy structure

Access hatch leading to central maintenance gantry, computer mainframe and storage areas

Oxygen tanks for life support

Specially designed seat with unique fold-down harness to secure crew members during high-g blast-off and re-entry

Cockpit. Thunderbird 3's cockpit can hold a crew of up to five, and the craft can be operated from any of these seats by a single crew member.

Flight control and navigation read-out. Pilot and navigator's display console shows navigation information and computations.

Nose attitude-control rockets

Fuel lines for retro-rockets

Retro-rockets. These are fired to reduce speed on approach to Thunderbird 5 and to enable re-entry into Earth's atmosphere.

Outer skin. This is coated with a heat-resistant ceramic layer to protect Thunderbird 3 during re-entry or rescue missions in the Sun's upper atmosphere.

Gravitron plates. These create artificial gravity inside the cockpit area, automatically adjusting the level of gravity as Thunderbird 3 travels through and beyond Earth's atmosphere.

Anti-detection device

Forward-pointing collision sensor. This provides warning of a potential collision with small objects. At high speeds the computer automatically diverts Thunderbird 3 to avoid any collision.

19

THUNDERBIRD 3

INTO SPACE WITH THE RED ARROW

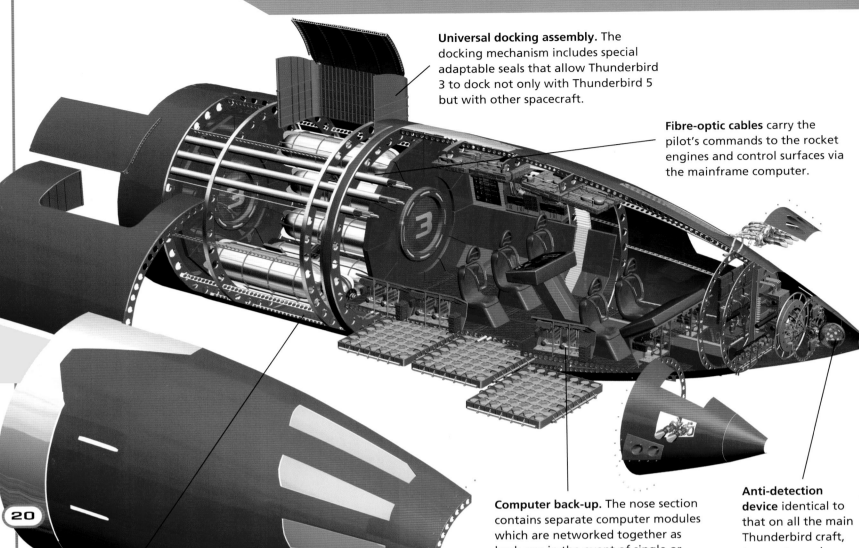

Universal docking assembly. The docking mechanism includes special adaptable seals that allow Thunderbird 3 to dock not only with Thunderbird 5 but with other spacecraft.

Fibre-optic cables carry the pilot's commands to the rocket engines and control surfaces via the mainframe computer.

Computer back-up. The nose section contains separate computer modules which are networked together as back-ups in the event of single or multiple failure of the computer mainframe housed in the main body.

Anti-detection device identical to that on all the main Thunderbird craft, to counter radar and other detection systems

Automatic sealing system. If ever the skin of the triple-hulled ship is holed or severely damaged, a self-sealing system is automatically triggered, releasing a special foam that prevents loss of air pressure inside the cockpit area.

Space lifeboat

In a dire emergency (for instance, if the main hull suffers fatal damage) the entire nose section of Thunderbird 3 can be detached from the rest of the body. It then serves as a lifeboat for the crew, allowing them to re-enter the Earth's atmosphere and return safely to the surface.

ARTIFICIAL GRAVITY

The first time Jeff Tracy heard the name of 'Brains' Hackenbacker was when he invented the 'gravitron plate' for use in NASA's spacecraft. This is a device that recreates the effect of gravity in localized areas. Jeff at once recognized Brains's true genius and offered him the chance to develop International Rescue following the death of Jeff's wife in an accident. Since leaving NASA Brains has further developed the gravitron plate so that it can now offer a gravity experience identical to that on Earth (current NASA gravitron plates can only recreate the effect of half of Earth's gravity). Only the cockpit of Thunderbird 3 is fitted with gravitron plates, as having zero-g in the rest of the ship makes maintenance and loading and unloading of Thunderbird 5's supplies easier.

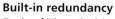
Jeff and the boys blast off in Thunderbird 3 to rescue John, who is alone on board Thunderbird 5, crippled by the Hood's missile. Little do they know that they are walking straight into the Hood's trap and putting their lives in deadly danger.

Built-in redundancy
Each of Thunderbird 3's main and buttress engines has a built-in 'redundancy facility'. This means that if any one of the engines fails or is destroyed in flight, Thunderbird 3 can still fly safely on the power of the remaining engines. In fact, Brains has designed the spacecraft so that it can return to Earth safely even if all three of its buttress engines are damaged in flight.

One-stage wonder
Thunderbird 3's unique design means that it can blast into space and return to Earth without the need for stages – sections of the rocket that are jettisoned during the flight to make the rocket lighter.

width 22 metres

length 85 metres

Feeling hot
During re-entry into the Earth's atmosphere, Thunderbird 3's fuselage has to endure temperatures of over 3000 °C (4500 °F). To stop the rocket from burning up, the fuselage is covered with a heat-resistant ceramic skin. Once safely in the atmosphere, the pilot can then fire up the rocket engines to bring Thunderbird 3 to a safe landing.

TECHNICAL DATA

Crew	up to 5
Length	85 metres (279 feet)
Width	
of fuselage	7 metres (25 feet)
across buttresses	22 metres (72 feet)
Weight	372 tonnes
Power source	Hackenbacker series 3000 fusion reactor
Range	unlimited
Engines	3 main engines (1 in each buttress) 3 secondary engines (located in central fuselage) 9 retro-rockets (located on buttresses) 10 attitude-control rockets
Launch thrust	1.8 million kg (4 million pounds)
Armaments	none

21

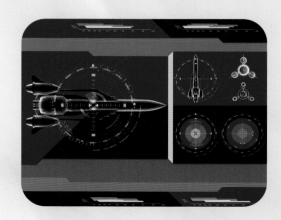

THUNDERBIRD 4

With three-quarters of the Earth's surface covered in water, it's not surprising that International Rescue's submarine rescue vehicle is on permanent standby in the secondary pod bay of Thunderbird 2. Its small size makes it ideal for underwater rescues, and when it cannot manage an emergency on its own, it can link up with other Thunderbird vehicles to bring people and vehicles to safety.

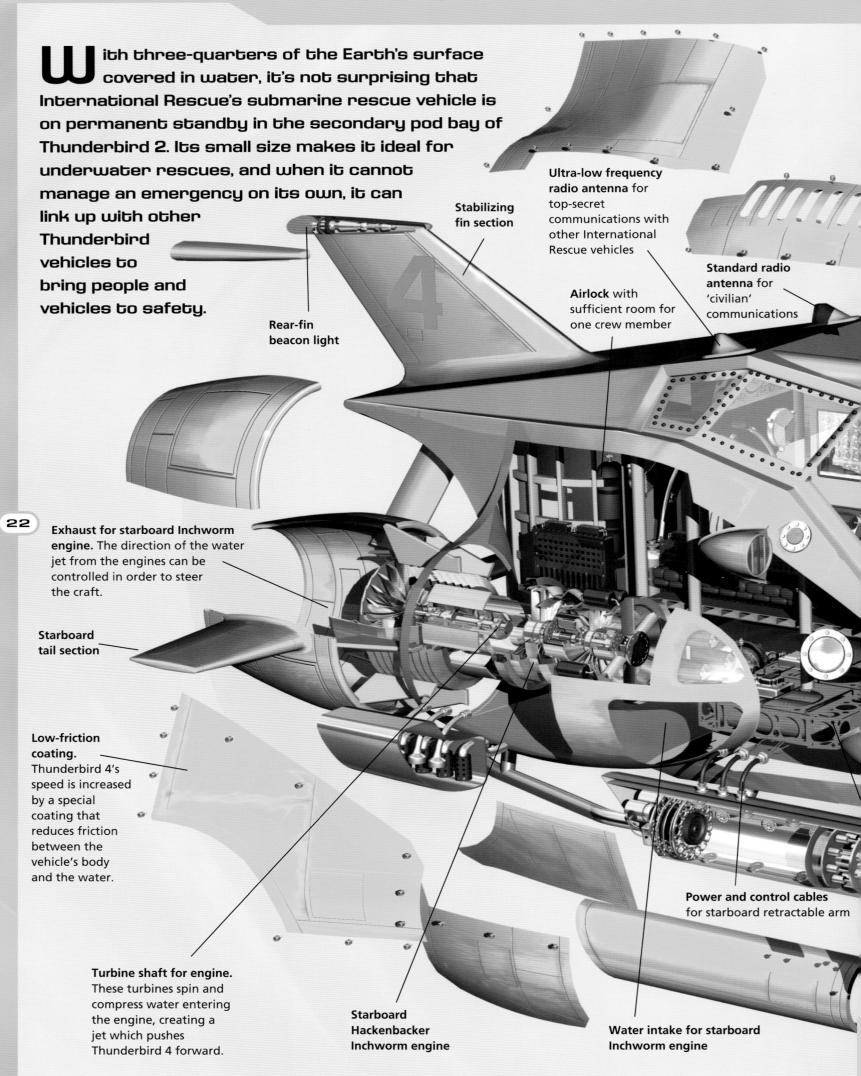

Stabilizing fin section

Ultra-low frequency radio antenna for top-secret communications with other International Rescue vehicles

Standard radio antenna for 'civilian' communications

Airlock with sufficient room for one crew member

Rear-fin beacon light

Exhaust for starboard Inchworm engine. The direction of the water jet from the engines can be controlled in order to steer the craft.

Starboard tail section

Low-friction coating. Thunderbird 4's speed is increased by a special coating that reduces friction between the vehicle's body and the water.

Power and control cables for starboard retractable arm

Turbine shaft for engine. These turbines spin and compress water entering the engine, creating a jet which pushes Thunderbird 4 forward.

Starboard Hackenbacker Inchworm engine

Water intake for starboard Inchworm engine

Creeping along

Thunderbird 4's fuel cell powers two Hackenbacker Inchworm engines (named after Brains's favourite insect). These use spinning turbines to draw in water and compress it to produce a high-pressure jet. This is shot out of the back of the craft to push it forward.

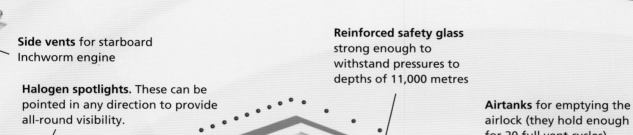

Side vents for starboard Inchworm engine

Halogen spotlights. These can be pointed in any direction to provide all-round visibility.

Titanium alloy framework

Reinforced safety glass strong enough to withstand pressures to depths of 11,000 metres

Airtanks for emptying the airlock (they hold enough for 20 full vent cycles)

Cockpit safety frame

Port retractable arm (with claw closed)

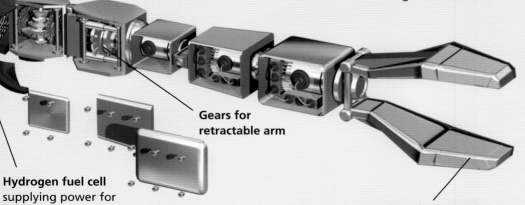

Cockpit controls and status display providing details of Thunderbird 4's performance

Opening for arm housing. This has a waterproof seal allowing retrieved objects to be brought inside Thunderbird 4.

Gears for retractable arm

Hydrogen fuel cell supplying power for Thunderbird 4's engines, computer and life-support systems

Starboard retractable arm (with claw open)

Lighting the way

Sunlight doesn't reach far beneath the water's surface, and below 150 metres everything is pitch black. In order to see at these depths, Thunderbird 4 is fitted with six halogen spotlights at the front of the craft. If a more stealthy approach is required or if the spotlights should fail, the heads-up display at the front of the cockpit can project what's in front of Thunderbird 4 using an image-intensifying system.

THUNDERBIRD 4

INTO THE DEEP WITH THE YELLOW SUBMERSIBLE

Gravity-free launch

Although it is normally stored in Thunderbird 2's secondary pod area, Thunderbird 4 can be launched directly into the sea from Tracy Island. Using a special track that has been laid with gravitron plates, the underwater craft can glide from its hangar and into the water. To facilitate the launch procedure, Brains ingeniously reversed the polarity of the gravitron plates, so allowing Thunderbird 4 to 'float' weightlessly into the water.

Thunderbird 4 splashes into the water after being released from Thunderbird 2's secondary pod area.

Water intakes are closed and lights are covered to prevent damage to fragile parts when Thunderbird 4 plunges into the water.

Up for any task

Since it was built at the Tracy Island automated production facility, Thunderbird 4 has been used for a variety of rescue missions, including recovering sailors from sunken vessels and patching up damaged oil tankers. It has also been used to explore the ocean depths and to observe the fascinating animals that live in the murky gloom.

FUEL CELL

At the core of Thunderbird 4 is its hydrogen fuel cell. As it moves along, the submarine draws in water and splits it into its basic parts – hydrogen and oxygen. The fuel cell then uses these to produce the power needed to drive the craft. This power supply is ultra-quiet and very friendly to the environment – the only waste product is water, created when the hydrogen and oxygen recombine.

In the absence of any of the regular International Rescue pilots, Alan Tracy guides Thunderbird 4 through the murky waters of London's River Thames to the rescue of hundreds of monorail passengers trapped after the Hood destroys the commuter track. Using the extended claws, Alan attaches grappling lines to the flooding train carriage so that it can be lifted clear by Thunderbird 2.

All-round visibility

The large panes of toughened plexiglass that enclose the cockpit of Thunderbird 4 provide the pilot with excellent visibility on three sides. To cover the remaining 'blind spot' to the rear of the craft, high-definition cameras send pictures to the cockpit.

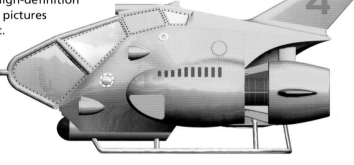

height 3.7 metres

Water wings

Just like an aeroplane, Thunderbird 4 has movable control surfaces on its wings and fin. These move as the pilot handles the controls, allowing the craft to perform complicated manoeuvres with precision.

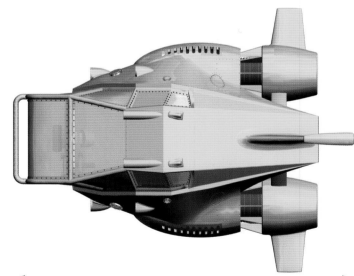

length 8 metres

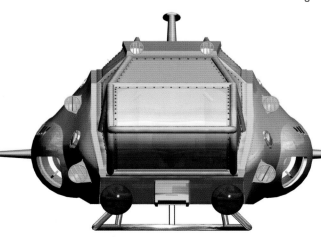

width 5 metres

Grabbing hands

At the front of Thunderbird 4 are two retractable claws. Although they are very simple in design and easy to operate, they are also extremely sensitive. They can perform the most delicate of operations, such as picking up fragile relics that have spent hundreds of years on the sea floor.

TECHNICAL DATA

Crew	1
Length	8 metres (26 feet)
Width including rear aquaplanes	5 metres (16.5 feet)
Height including rear rudder	3.7 metres (12 feet)
Weight	13 tonnes
Power source	hydrogen fuel cell power plant
Maximum speed underwater	278 km/h (173 mph)
surface	185 km/h (115 mph)
Maximum diving depth	11,000 metres (36,090 feet)
Engines	2 Hackenbacker Inchworm engines
Armaments	none

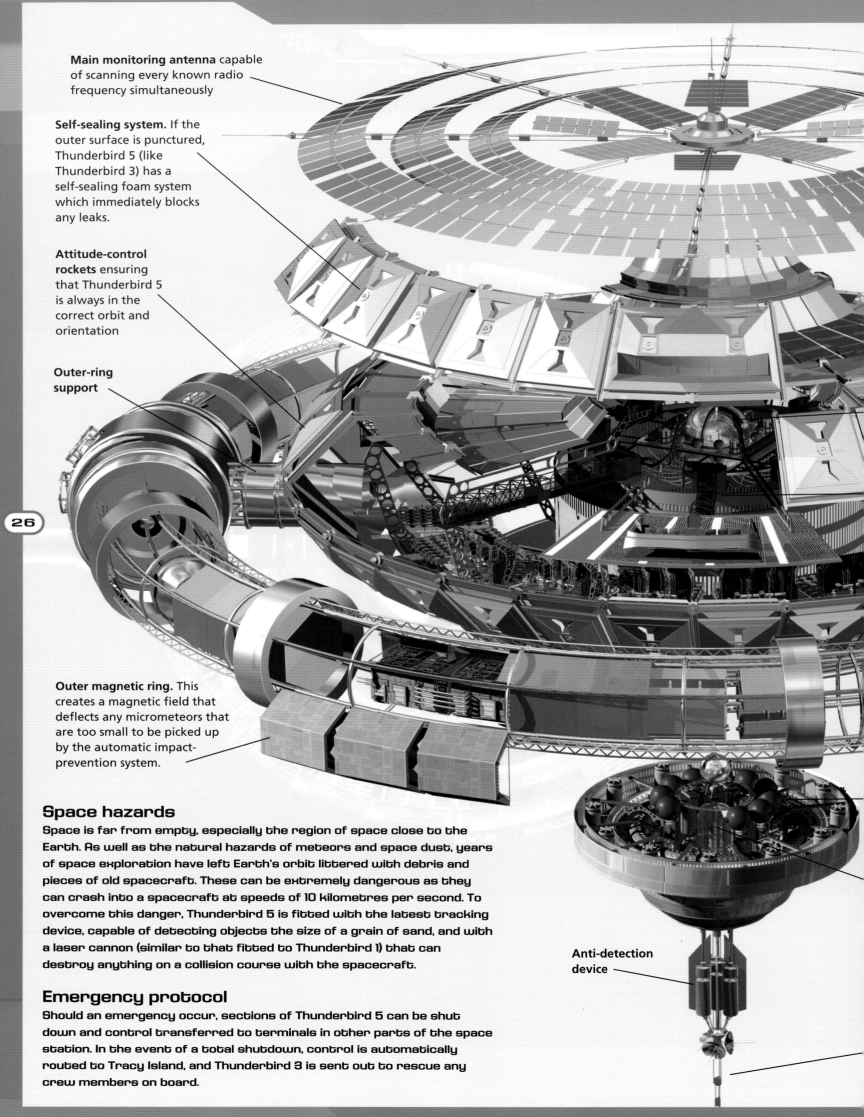

Main monitoring antenna capable of scanning every known radio frequency simultaneously

Self-sealing system. If the outer surface is punctured, Thunderbird 5 (like Thunderbird 3) has a self-sealing foam system which immediately blocks any leaks.

Attitude-control rockets ensuring that Thunderbird 5 is always in the correct orbit and orientation

Outer-ring support

Outer magnetic ring. This creates a magnetic field that deflects any micrometeors that are too small to be picked up by the automatic impact-prevention system.

Anti-detection device

Space hazards

Space is far from empty, especially the region of space close to the Earth. As well as the natural hazards of meteors and space dust, years of space exploration have left Earth's orbit littered with debris and pieces of old spacecraft. These can be extremely dangerous as they can crash into a spacecraft at speeds of 10 kilometres per second. To overcome this danger, Thunderbird 5 is fitted with the latest tracking device, capable of detecting objects the size of a grain of sand, and with a laser cannon (similar to that fitted to Thunderbird 1) that can destroy anything on a collision course with the spacecraft.

Emergency protocol

Should an emergency occur, sections of Thunderbird 5 can be shut down and control transferred to terminals in other parts of the space station. In the event of a total shutdown, control is automatically routed to Tracy Island, and Thunderbird 3 is sent out to rescue any crew members on board.

26

JOHN TRACY – age 22
• space monitor in charge of Thunderbird 5
• a computer whizz kid and an ideal choice for monitoring and maintaining Thunderbird 5's mainframe computer

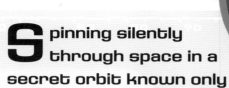

Spinning silently through space in a secret orbit known only to International Rescue and a few select members of NASA is Thunderbird 5. Like an eye that never sleeps, it is the hub for International Rescue's communications, continually scanning the airwaves for distress calls and signs of trouble. In conjunction with a network of top-secret satellites, Thunderbird 5 is able to keep a close watch on any part of the world and to send information to Tracy Island and any Thunderbird craft instantly.

Inner habitation ring containing living quarters and monitoring stations

Hackenbacker series 3000 fusion reactor supplying heat to main generators

Access gantry to fusion core allowing access for routine maintenance and repairs

Extendable docking assembly gantry allowing access to Thunderbird 5

Tanks storing reactor coolant. This super-cooled fluid is pumped around the reactor core to prevent overheating and meltdown.

Universal docking assembly providing an airtight seal with any visiting spacecraft

Main generator. This provides power to life-support systems, computers, monitoring devices and impact-prevention system.

Lonely job

Manning Thunderbird 5 is a lonely job and constantly monitoring emergencies is tiring work. To keep John Tracy amused during his tours of duty in space, Thunderbird 5 is fitted with the latest entertainment systems, including games consoles and a home cinema. It is also fitted with gravitron plates that recreate the gravity of Earth's surface to make life in space as comfortable as possible. A tour of duty for John lasts three weeks. After this, Thunderbird 3 arrives to take him back to the surface for a week's rest and relaxation on Tracy Island before he returns to his monitoring duties.

Broadcasting antenna. This sends signals to International Rescue craft and Tracy Island using secure frequencies.

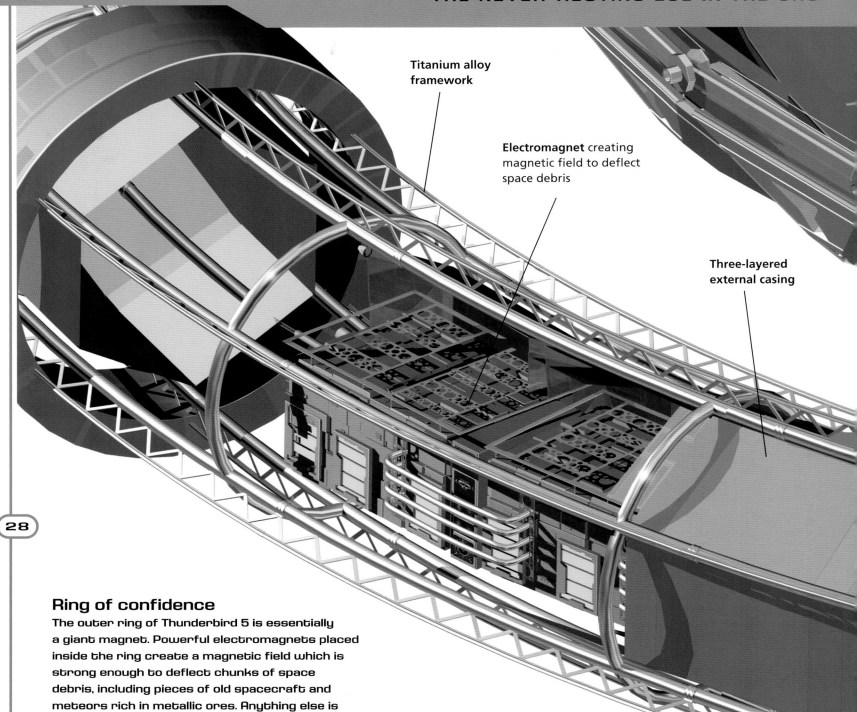

Titanium alloy framework

Electromagnet creating magnetic field to deflect space debris

Three-layered external casing

28

Ring of confidence

The outer ring of Thunderbird 5 is essentially a giant magnet. Powerful electromagnets placed inside the ring create a magnetic field which is strong enough to deflect chunks of space debris, including pieces of old spacecraft and meteors rich in metallic ores. Anything else is dealt with by the space station's laser cannon.

IN HIDING

Thunderbird 5 is fitted with the standard anti-detection devices found on other International Rescue vehicles, but it also has extra systems to escape detection by telescopes and other devices used in astronomy, which might accidentally reveal the monitoring station's location. The anti-detection equipment fitted to the underside of Thunderbird 5 is able to reduce its 'visibility' to the entire range of electromagnetic radiation, from microwaves to radio waves.

When the Hood's missile slams into Thunderbird 5, it sets off a catastrophic chain of events. Jeff Tracy blasts off with his sons to rescue John, leaving their island headquarters unguarded and exposed. As control of both Thunderbirds 3 and 5 switches to Tracy Island – now in the hands of the Hood – the evil mastermind is able to take over the two spacecraft, leaving them helpless as they begin their fiery and fatal descent into the Earth's atmosphere.

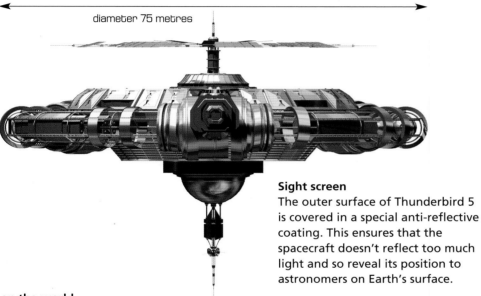

diameter 75 metres

Sight screen
The outer surface of Thunderbird 5 is covered in a special anti-reflective coating. This ensures that the spacecraft doesn't reflect too much light and so reveal its position to astronomers on Earth's surface.

Ear on the world
Fitted on top of Thunderbird 5 is the enormous main monitoring antenna. This huge disc picks up radio signals on all wavelengths, including secure frequencies used by military and emergency services. The antenna also collects signals from International Rescue's top-secret network of smaller monitoring satellites, which are in orbit over other parts of the globe. All these signals are routed through the space station's mainframe computer, which analyses the data, filtering out non-emergency signals.

Piece by piece
Thunderbird 5's enormous bulk was too large to be blasted into space in one piece. Instead, it was built in sections at the Tracy Island production facility and assembled in orbit using Thunderbird 3.

length 108 metres

TECHNICAL DATA

Crew	usually 1, but can support up to 5
Diameter	75 metres (246 feet)
Length including docking port	108 metres (354 feet)
Height including scanning arrays	69 metres (226 feet)
Weight	869 tonnes
Power source	Hackenbacker series 3000 fusion reactor
Engines	1 booster rocket (to lift Thunderbird 5 to a higher orbit) 32 attitude-control rockets (for minor position adjustments)
Orbit	geostationary orbit, 35,790 km (22,226 miles) above the Pacific Ocean
Armaments	multi-barrelled cannon

FAB 1

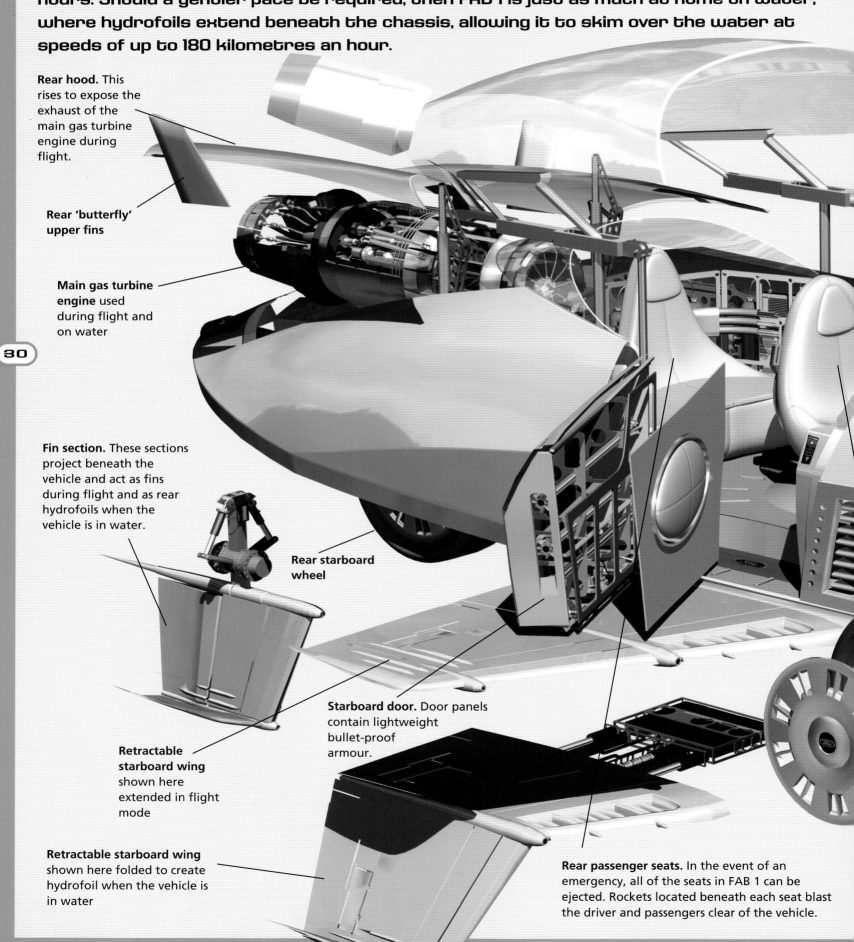

Cruising serenely along the roads around her English country estate, Lady Penelope Creighton-Ward's luxury six-wheeled saloon is a common – and dazzling – sight. But few people who see the car would guess what lies beneath the bonnet. At the flick of a switch, Lady Penelope's chauffeur, Parker, can transform the saloon, code-named FAB 1, into a supersonic jet, capable of carrying her ladyship to Tracy Island in a matter of hours. Should a gentler pace be required, then FAB 1 is just as much at home on water, where hydrofoils extend beneath the chassis, allowing it to skim over the water at speeds of up to 180 kilometres an hour.

Rear hood. This rises to expose the exhaust of the main gas turbine engine during flight.

Rear 'butterfly' upper fins

Main gas turbine engine used during flight and on water

30

Fin section. These sections project beneath the vehicle and act as fins during flight and as rear hydrofoils when the vehicle is in water.

Rear starboard wheel

Retractable starboard wing shown here extended in flight mode

Starboard door. Door panels contain lightweight bullet-proof armour.

Retractable starboard wing shown here folded to create hydrofoil when the vehicle is in water

Rear passenger seats. In the event of an emergency, all of the seats in FAB 1 can be ejected. Rockets located beneath each seat blast the driver and passengers clear of the vehicle.

Plexiglass canopy. This is fully retractable, and in an extreme emergency it is blasted clear before the driver and passenger seats are ejected.

Plexiglass windscreen. During flight, the heads-up display (HUD) is projected onto a small visor that drops down from Parker's cap, allowing him to keep up to date with the vehicle's performance without taking his eyes off the skies.

LADY PENELOPE – age classified
• international agent
• can trace her family back nearly 1000 years, owns estates in England and France
• entitled to a seat in the House of Lords (upper house of the British government)

Is it a bird?

Being an agent for International Rescue can take you to all parts of the world, and a lady simply has to look her best if she's to make the right impression. So the only way to travel is to fly – first class, of course. Using the lifting-body technology featured in Thunderbird 2, Brains was able to create a design that could go from luxury saloon to supersonic jet with the minimum of fuss.

Bonnet

Bonnet air intake

Secondary gas turbine engine used to power wheels during road-driving and hover jets during flight

81

Front grille

Front mini-gun port

Driver's display. Digital readouts display road or flight data to the driver/pilot.

Yolk-style steering wheel

Centrally located driver's seat

Hover jets. Located in each of the six wheels, these are fully movable, allowing the pilot to hover or to fly slowly in any direction.

Fully movable halogen lights. These act as headlights while the vehicle is on the road, and can double as spotlights.

Universal car registration plate FAB 1. This plate has registration clearance in all countries of the world, allowing Lady Penelope to pass unhindered by local law officers.

Ford

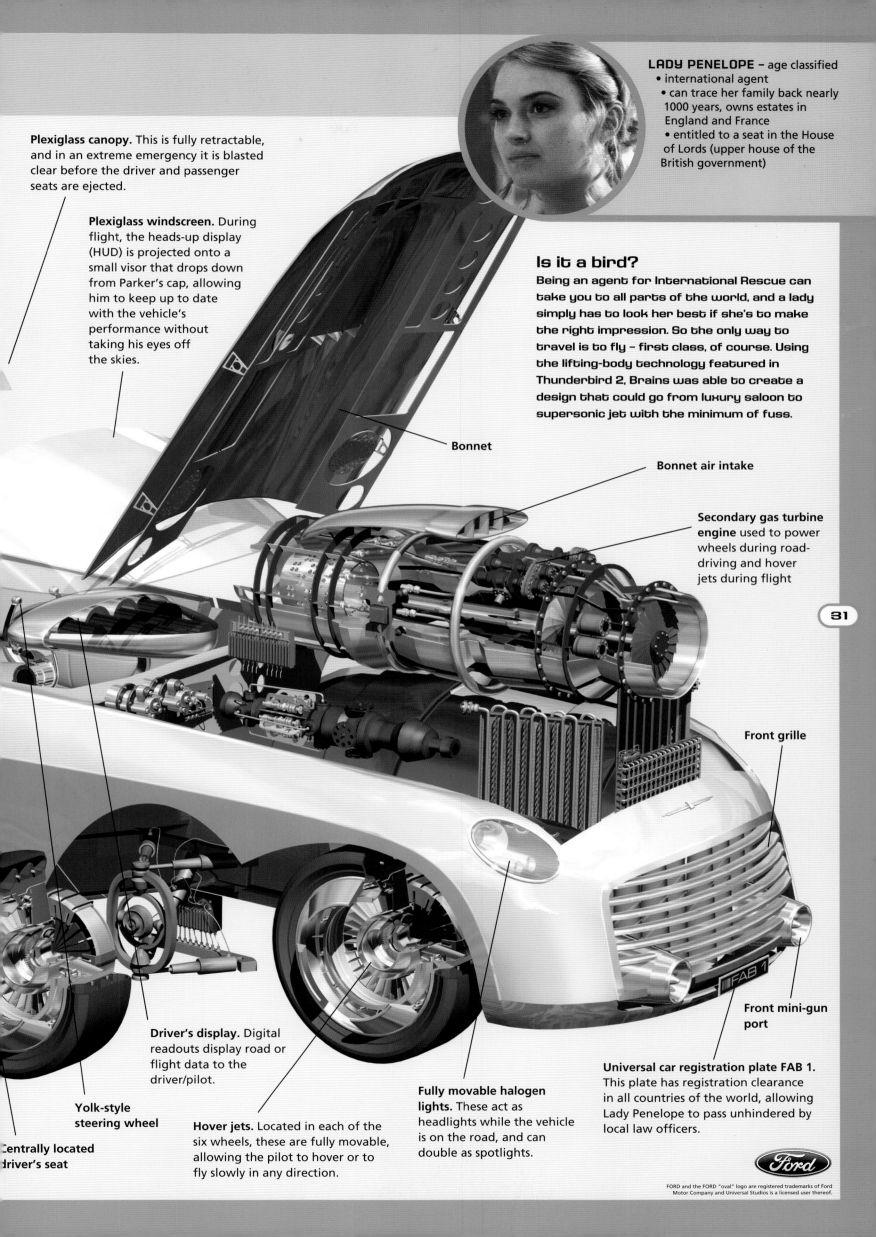

FAB 1

Flying car

Combining a busy social life with her role as an International Rescue agent takes Lady Penelope to some of the most glamorous places in the world (as well as a few that leave a lot to be desired). Whatever the occasion, however, FAB 1 ensures that she arrives in the height of luxury – and always on time. FAB 1's flight capabilities mean that Lady Penelope can cross to the other side of the world in a matter of hours, cruising high above the ground at supersonic speeds.

Front grille serving as air intake for the gas turbine engine

32

Tail section in raised position

Armed to the teeth

Beneath the sleek exterior of the luxury car is a powerful arsenal of weapons. At the front, FAB 1 is equipped with twin high-velocity mini-guns (with a third at the rear), and there are two heat-seeking rockets buried beneath the front wings. If FAB 1 is attacked while on water, there are two mini-torpedo tubes located just beneath the main engine compartment.

Wheels angled downward during flight

Proof against bullet and bomb

For defence against missile attack, FAB 1 is fitted not only with chaff and flare dispensers but also with an electronic counter-measure (ECM) device. This can disrupt a missile's guidance system and even turn it back against its firer. More obvious measures include a smoke canister, bullet-proof glass, and lightweight armour-plating in all body panels.

HOVER JETS

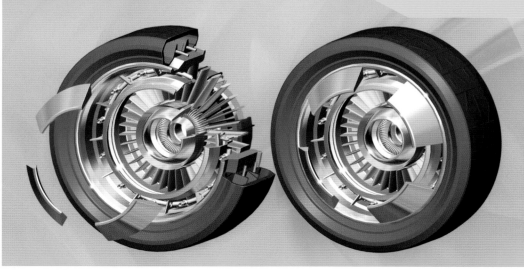

While puzzling over how to give FAB 1 VTOL (vertical take-off and landing) capability, Brains Hackenbacker came up with an ingenious solution – to combine the wheels with the jet exhausts. When Parker transforms FAB 1 to flight mode, the wheels fold under the vehicle's chassis, turning into the downward-pointing exhausts for the VTOL engines.

As part of his training as driver/pilot of FAB 1, Parker spent a season racing powerboats around the world. The experience proved invaluable, as handling the vessel at breathtaking speeds over water is now second nature to the deadpan chauffeur. Sadly, even Parker's skills are not up to the job of dodging the Hood's torpedoes. Thanks to Brains, though, FAB 1 is fitted with a number of back-up systems to ensure the safety of its passengers.

Water wings

Another of Brains's brilliant ideas was to transform FAB 1's wings into hydrofoils for travel on water. These hydrofoils lift the vehicle's body clear of the water, meaning that less of the craft is in contact with the water. This reduces friction and allows FAB 1 to travel much faster than a conventional boat.

width 2.1 metres

Tails up
The central sections of FAB 1's boot are raised during flight to expose the gas turbine engine and to act as the tail section.

Car for all seasons
On FAB 1's underside there is a set of retractable skis that enable the vehicle to travel across heavy snow. The bulletproof, run-flat tyres are fitted with studs that give extra grip in icy conditions.

length 7.9 metres

Floating sanctuary
The central passenger compartment of FAB 1 doubles as an emergency life raft in the event of an emergency at sea. Buoyancy tanks hidden in the body panelling ensure that the compartment remains afloat after it has broken away from the rest of the vehicle.

Folding wheels
During flight, the rear set of wheels folds into the vehicle's body completely. This prevents them from creating unnecessary drag and so slowing the aircraft down.

wingspan 4.7 metres

TECHNICAL DATA

Crew	1 pilot/driver
	plus 3 passengers
Length	7.9 metres (26 feet)
Width	2.1 metres (7 feet)
with hydrofoils	
extended	3.5 metres (11.5 feet)
Wingspan	4.7 metres (15.5 feet)
Height	1.68 metres (5.5 feet)
Weight	3.4 tonnes
Power source	Hackenbacker series 3000 nuclear fusion reactor (miniature version)
Maximum speed	
land	320 km/h (199 mph)
sea	185 km/h (115 mph)
air	9120 km/h (5664 mph)
Engines	1 gas turbine jet engine
	6 mini hover engines (located in wheels)
Armaments	3 high-velocity mini-guns (2 at front, 1 at rear)
	2 heat-seeking rockets
	2 mini torpedo tubes